GW00367677

MARVEL

WHAT WOULD HULK DO?

A STUDIO PRESS BOOK

First published in the UK in 2021 by Studio Press,
an imprint of Bonnier Books UK Limited,
4th Floor, Victoria House, Bloomsbury Square, London, WC1B 4DA
Owned by Bonnier Books,
Sveavägen 56, Stockholm, Sweden

www.bonnierbooks.co.uk

1 3 5 7 9 10 8 6 4 2

ISBN 978-1-80078-030-9

Written by Susie Rae
Edited by Sophie Blackman and Saaleh Patel
Designed by Rob Ward
Production by Emma Kidd

A CIP catalogue for this book is available from the British Library

Printed and bound in Italy

WHAT WOULD HULK DO?

WORKING OUT...

HULK VERY GOOD AT WORKING OUT.
HERE IS HULK'S WORKOUT PLAN:

1. PICK UP TRUCK IN EACH HAND.
2. MAKE SURE TO BEND KNEES. LIFT TRUCK.
3. THROW IT AS HARD AS POSSIBLE.

HULK VERY STRONG, SO FOR PEOPLE
WHO ARE PUNY LIKE THOR, IT OKAY TO
START WITH SOMETHING LIGHTER,
LIKE CAR OR HELPFUL PASSER-BY.

MAKE SURE TO COOL
DOWN AFTERWARDS
BY UPROOTING SMALL TREE.

GETTING A HAIRCUT...

NO NEED TO PAY FOR FANCY
HAIRCUT — IT JUST GROW BACK.
HULK CUT OWN HAIR USING
UPSIDE-DOWN BOWL AND ENTHUSIASM.

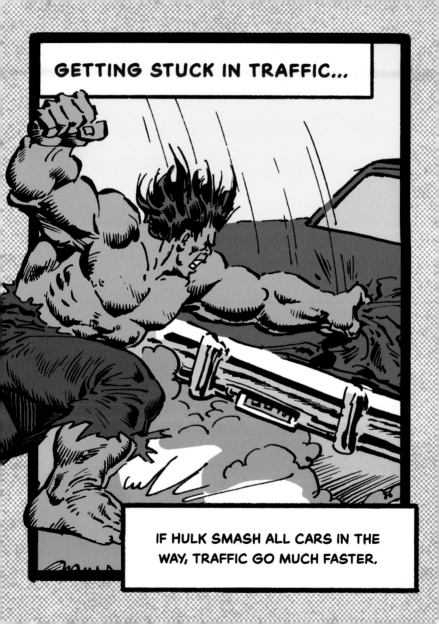

RECYCLING...

HULK IS EXPERT AT GOING
GREEN. RECYCLING VERY
GOOD FOR THE PLANET...

... SO HE USE OLD BITS OF FURNITURE
OR EMPTY FOOD TINS TO THROW
AT PEOPLE WHO USE TOO MUCH
SINGLE-USE PLASTIC.

... BY THROWING THEM GREAT DISTANCE.

FACING YOUR FEARS...

HULK FIND IT BEST TO CONFRONT FEARS HEAD-ON. ALL HE NEED TO FACE FEARS IS BRAVERY, STRENGTH...

... AND ENOUGH GAMMA RADIATION IN BLOODSTREAM THAT HE MUCH SCARIER THAN EVERYTHING ELSE.

HOUSEWORK...

HULK OFTEN HAVE TO RENOVATE HIS
HOUSE, AS IT GET SMASHED UP IN
BATTLES WITH SUPER VILLAINS A LOT.

IF SOMETHING GET DIRTY,
BEST SOLUTION IS TO BREAK
IT AND WAIT FOR DR BANNER
TO REPLACE IT WITH NEW ONE.

ACADEMIA...

TEAMWORK...

WORKING TOGETHER AND ASKING
FOR HELP ARE IMPORTANT PART OF
ACHIEVING GOALS IN WORKPLACE.

HULK FIND THE OTHER AVENGERS VERY
USEFUL FOR TASKS LIKE PICKING UP THINGS
THAT HULK THROW, GIVING HULK NEW
THINGS TO THROW AND FETCHING SNACKS.

FINE DINING...

WHEN DINNER IS INTERRUPTED BY SUPER VILLAIN ATTACK, NICE RESTAURANTS USUALLY HAVE LOTS OF THINGS TO THROW.

CORRECT ETIQUETTE IS TO START BY THROWING CUTLERY ON OUTSIDE AND WORK IN — HULK WON'T EMBARRASS HIMSELF AND DO IN WRONG ORDER.

BEING A SPORTS FAN...
HULK DON'T FOLLOW MANY SPORT, BECAUSE HE ONLY WANT TO WATCH SPORT HE NOT GOOD AT HIMSELF, OTHERWISE IT GET BORING.
THIS A PROBLEM FOR HULK, BECAUSE HE MUCH FASTER AND STRONGER THAN ANY PUNY HUMAN...
... APART FROM ICE DANCERS. THEY SPIN MUCH FASTER THAN HULK CAN SPIN, AND HE RESPECT THAT.

LIVING WITH ROOMMATES...

ONE OF MOST COMMON
ARGUMENTS WITH ROOMMATES
IS WHAT TEMPERATURE
TO KEEP HOUSE AT.

DR BANNER LIKE TEMPERATURE HOT.
HULK LIKE TEMPERATURE COLD.

COMPROMISE BY RIPPING THERMOSTAT
OUT OF WALL AND YELLING.

BUYING COFFEE...

COFFEE SHOP LIE. FLAT WHITE NOT EVEN FLAT, AND WHEN HULK SMASH CUP TO MAKE IT FLAT, THEY ASK HULK TO LEAVE AND NOT COME BACK.

DR BANNER NOT HAPPY ABOUT THIS, BECAUSE HE LIKE THAT COFFEE SHOP. HULK ADVISE HIM TO BE MORE SPECIFIC IN COFFEE ORDER.

FAMILY DISPUTES...

MOST FAMILY DISPUTES BEST RESOLVED BY HONESTLY EXPRESSING FEELINGS.

EVEN WHEN HULK ACCIDENTALLY TURNED COUSIN GREEN THROUGH BLOOD TRANSFUSION, FAMILY WERE MOSTLY VERY UNDERSTANDING.

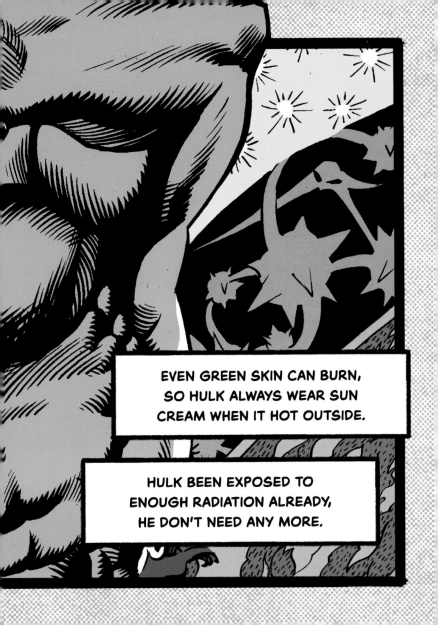

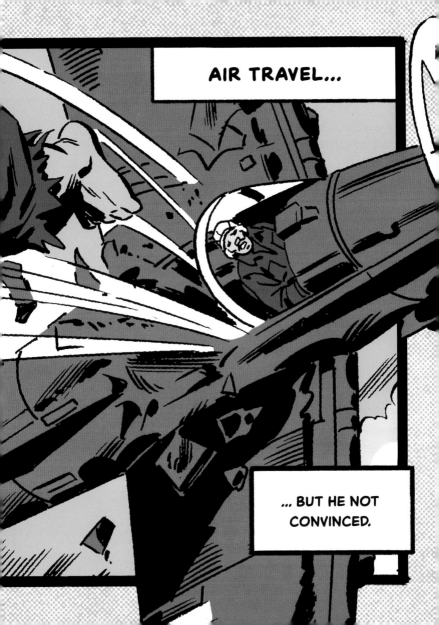

OTHER MARVEL BOOKS...

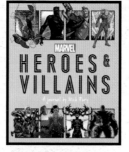